Making Pe

in practice and poetry

Making Peace

in practice and poetry

A workbook for small groups or individual use

Joy Mead

WILD GOOSE PUBLICATIONS

First published 2004 by

Wild Goose Publications, 4th Floor, Savoy House, 140 Sauchiehall St,
Glasgow G2 3DH, UK.
Wild Goose Publications is the publishing division of the Iona Community.
Scottish Charity No. SCO03794. Limited Company Reg. No. SCO96243.
www.ionabooks.com

ISBN 1 901557 84 7

Cover illustration: String of peace flags © Wahaba Karuna
http://www.karunaarts.com

A catalogue record for this book is available from the British Library.

Overseas distribution:
Australia: Willow Connection Pty Ltd, Unit 4A, 3-9 Kenneth Road, Manly Vale, NSW 2093
New Zealand: Pleroma, Higginson Street, Otane 4170, Central Hawkes Bay
Canada: Novalis Publishing & Distribution, 49 Front Street East, Toronto, Ontario M5E 1B3

Permission to reproduce any part of this work in Australia or New Zealand should be
sought from Willow Connection.

Printed by Bell & Bain, Thornliebank, Glasgow

Contents

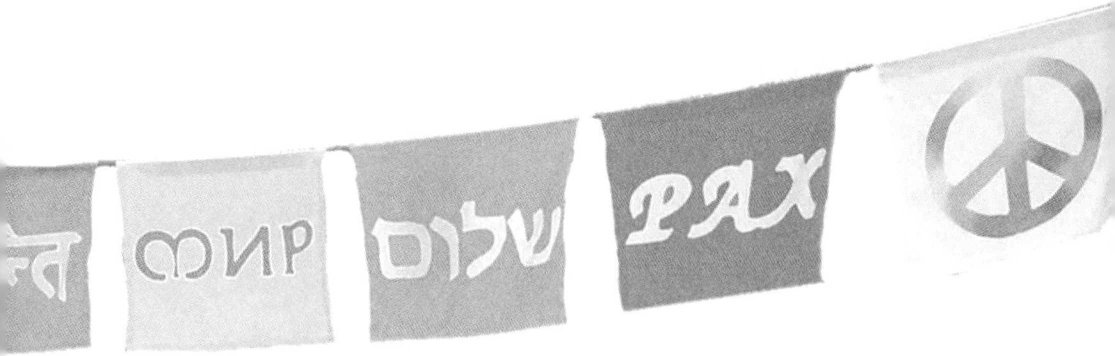
МИР
שלום
PAX

Personal peacemaking

Today I shall try to make peace
in practice and poetry.
I shall choose words and images carefully,
avoiding all that proscribes, restricts,
oppresses, destroys, humiliates, patronises, enslaves.

I shall fight no fights, not even 'good' ones.
I shall not stand up for Jesus
    or be a soldier of anything –
    not even the cross;
I shall not
    wave any flaming swords;
I shall address no-one as Lord
    or mighty conqueror;
I shall not put on any sort of armour,
    not even the armour of Christ
    or the dressings of power.
I shall not march for Jesus
or anyone else.
I shall parade no nationalistic flags,
nor bang any triumphalist drums.

I shall be a pilgrim
and try to walk lightly

for the sake of the earth,
and the life it sustains;

I shall try to use words
that open minds
and stretch imaginations;
words that show an alternative
to famine, war, racism, torture, unjust structures,
unjust trading systems, violence, war,
all that denies life.

I may write about sex
or about violence
but I will resist the media urge
to conflate the two.

I shall ask questions that stir the heart,
motivate the will,
stretch the imagination,
widen the moral vision,
so that life in all its fullness,
diversity and wonder will be cherished
on this fragile and finite planet.

I shall make this day, and every day,
        a holy day;
I shall work, share, play and touch
within a circle of wholeness.

I shall resist violence and destruction
creatively by:
      dancing and laughing,
      planting trees and sowing seeds,
      making and sharing bread
      … and ice cream!
      lighting candles,
      allowing my body to absorb the peace
         of artists like Chagall, Vermeer, Winifred Nicholson,
      being alive to story, song and symbol,
         touch and scent.

I shall not abandon reason
but I shall know its limits
and resist the relentless course of logic.

I shall value imagination.

I shall try to understand compassion
and feel another's pain
as if it were my own.

I shall develop my own understanding of prayer,
share it with others
and enable them to explore
their own understandings.

I shall look more

and listen more.
I shall live more moments
as given moments.

I shall make mistakes
and admit to them humbly.

Today I shall dream –
of people together,
loving, sharing, eating, dancing.

And at the end of the day,
when things are much the same,
I shall continue to hope.
I shall remember that the personal
is always political; that inner peace
cannot be separated from wholeness
and health in community;
that small acts of beauty
by small groups of people
still carry the potential
to change the world.

Joy Mead

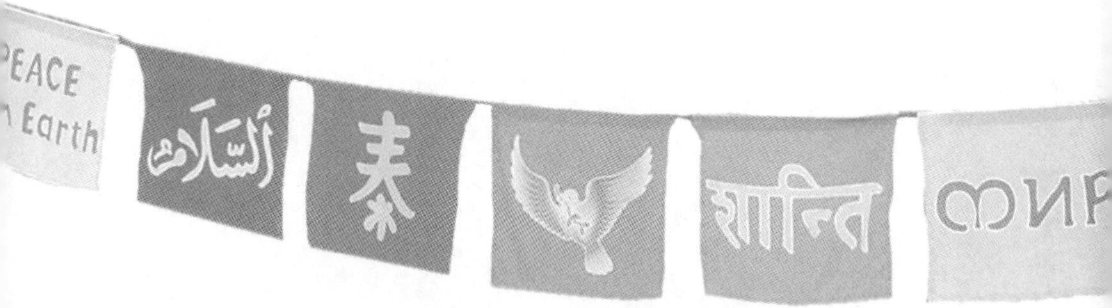
PEACE
n Earth
السلام
शान्ति
МИР

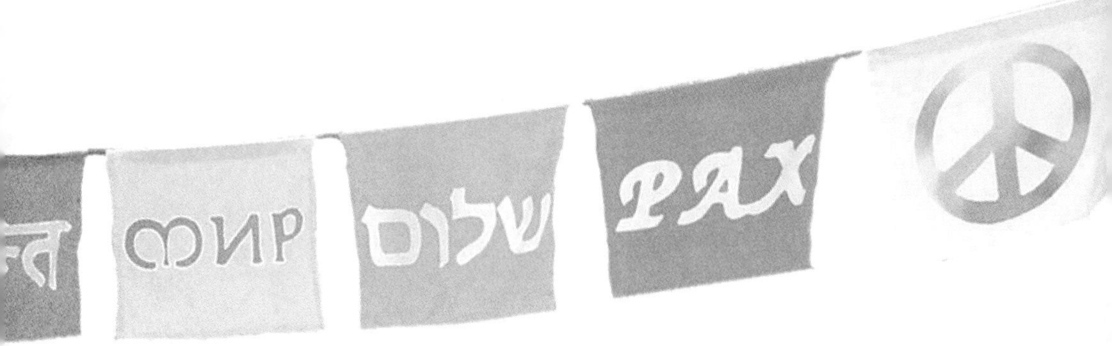
МИР
שלום
PAX

Introduction

This material, designed for small groups but also suitable for individual use, is intended to enhance our understanding of poetry in everyday life. It will probably be most appropriate for groups and individuals who enjoy creative writing or who would like to develop their writing skills, but other language-based activities are included. Workshop leaders will need to look carefully at the way the time available is used and possibly spread the material over more than one meeting.

In the five sessions, we will look at the potential of the words we choose and the images we use. We are all poets when we attempt to express the essence of our particular experience: when, for example, we explore how best to show the blue of bluebells, the trust of a newborn baby, the touch of a lover ... Through language we discover what it means to be human. We live in culture as much as nature and mediate, explore, understand, create our world through language and imagination. Words express and shape what we are, what we might become, how we relate to all life, how we see our world. Each of us has the potential to be creative or aggressive, gentle or violent, vulnerable or oppressive. We use language positively to question, remember, repair, reconcile, transform, create and liberate.

Making peace begins with understanding ourselves: the way we think, listen, see; how we relate to others. Peace is a process from exclusiveness to inclusiveness, from aggression to gentleness, from reconciliation to transformation ... and its beginning may be in our acceptance of uncertainty and confusion.

Our overall aim in these sessions is to become wiser in the way we choose and use words and to see more clearly how life is ... and how it could be transformed.

One

Let us be different

Let us be different

Aim:

To explore our needs and longings.

Preparation:

You will need:
- Pens and paper
- A flip chart
- At least one copy (or postcards) of the painting: *Sunday Afternoon on the Island of the Grande Jatte* by Georges Seurat.

Welcome:

Make sure people know one another and are at ease. Be ready to serve tea and coffee.

Introduction:

Exploring our needs and longings is a huge and complex subject; we can only touch upon certain aspects of it in this workshop.

We will look at the creative ways we might express our needs and longings, whilst being aware of and respecting the needs and longings of others. Within that sense of our humanness which holds us together, we hope to discover a common humanity, a unity in difference and a peace we can own.

Read this paragraph from the short story *Kew Gardens* by Virginia Woolf:

Thus one couple after another with much the same irregular and aimless movement passed the flower-bed and were enveloped in layer after layer of green-blue vapour, in which at first their bodies had substance and a dash of colour, but later both substance and the colour dissolved in the green-blue atmosphere. How hot it was! So hot that even the thrush chose to hop, like a mechanical bird, in the shadow of the flowers, with long pauses between one movement and the next; instead of rambling vaguely the white butterflies danced one above another making with their white shifting flakes the outline of a shattered marble column above the tallest flowers; the glass roofs of the palm house shone as if a whole market full of shiny green umbrellas had opened in the sun; and in the drone of the aeroplane the voice of the summer sky murmured its fierce soul. Yellow and black, pink and snow white, shapes of all these colours, men, women and children, were spotted for a second upon the horizon and then seeing the breadth of yellow that lay upon the grass, they wavered and sought shade beneath the trees, dissolving like drops of water in the yellow and green atmosphere, staining it faintly with red and blue. It seemed as if all gross and heavy bodies had sunk down in the heat motionless and lay huddled upon the ground, but their voices went wavering from them as if they were flames lolling from the thick waxen bodies of candles. Voices, yes, voices, wordless voices, breaking the silence suddenly with such depth of contentment, such passion of desire, or, in the voices of children, such freshness of surprise; breaking the silence? But there was no silence; all the time the motor omnibuses were turning their wheels and changing their gear; like a vast nest of Chinese boxes all wrought steel turning ceaselessly one within another the city murmured; on top of which the voices cried aloud and the petals of myriads of flowers flashed their colours into the air.

What do you see?

People are together yet separate ... at one with their natural surroundings, yet somehow apart from them. Virginia Woolf doesn't wipe out difference but attempts to make a whole with all difference intact.

Now look at the painting *Sunday Afternoon on the Island of the Grande Jatte.*

George Seurat's painting has an unmistakable poetic quality. Like the story, the painting shows us a scene of apparent calm. But what is going on beneath the surface of calm – beneath the surface of the lives of these stiffly urban people out together in the fresh air yet intent on ignoring one another? Neither the story nor the painting speaks specifically of needs and longings and yet ...

Talk about this.

Read this extract from *If This is a Man* by Nobel Prize winning writer and holocaust survivor Primo Levi, who relates with clarity and gentleness the story of his time in a concentration camp in Poland. In this extract, the Italian prisoners have just arrived at the camp:

We know that we will have difficulty in being understood, and this is as it should be. But consider what value, what meaning is enclosed even in the smallest of our daily habits, in the hundred possessions which even the poorest beggar owns: a handkerchief, an old letter, the photo of a cherished person. These things are part of us, almost like the limbs of our body; nor is it conceivable that we can be deprived of them in our world, for we immediately find others to substitute the old ones, other objects which are ours in their personification and evocation of our memories.

Imagine a man who is deprived of everyone he loves, and at the same time of his house, his habits, his clothes, in short, of everything he possesses: he will be a hollow man, reduced to suffering and needs, forgetful of dignity and restraint, for he who loses all often easily loses himself. He will be a man whose life or death can be lightly decided with no sense of human affinity, in the most fortunate of cases, on the pure judgement of utility. It is in this way that one can understand the double sense of the term 'extermination camp', and it is now clear what we seek to express with the phrase: 'to lie on the bottom.'

Talk about the various interpretations of the word 'need' in this situation.

Think about our need to discover in things a value beyond extrinsic or monetary worth.

What happens when we communicate our needs to others ... and when we don't?

We need words to keep us human:

Our needs are made of words: they come to us in speech, and they can die for lack of expression. Without a public language to help us find our own words, our needs will dry up in silence. It is words only, the common meanings they bear, which give me the right to speak in the name of the strangers at my door. Without a language adequate to this moment we risk losing ourselves in *resignation towards the portion of life which has been allotted to us. Without the light of language, we risk becoming strangers to our better selves.*

(from *The Needs of Strangers* by Michael Ignatieff)

Needs that are silenced or lack a language for their expression may cease to be felt. What then? What happens when you cease to feel? Think about this in relation to Primo Levi's story. What happens to kindness, compassion, gentleness and caring in the appalling conditions of a concentration camp where survival becomes the paramount need?

Now think about these qualities in ordinary, everyday life. How do the words sound when set up against words like power, strength, might, ambition, stoicism? … Do they sound ineffective, even silly? Do they prevent us from being objective? How do *you* value objectivity?

Need or greed?

What are our essential needs? This question may be difficult to answer. Clearly, they won't separate tidily into material needs on one hand and spiritual needs on the other.

Imagine you are forced to leave your home with no time to prepare. You are allowed to take with you five useful things and one that is of no practical use. What do your choices say about you and your needs?

E.F. Schumacher (*Small is Beautiful*) advocated a culture of simplicity based on an understanding that the basic needs of human beings are limited and attainable. It's greed that's unlimited.

Manfred Max-Neef, a specialist in human-scale development, identifies nine basic needs:

Subsistence – creation, health, food, shelter, skills, work, feedback
Protection – security, society
Affection – friendship, family, love
Understanding – curiosity, education
Participation – responsibilities, interaction, community
Leisure – play, fantasy, intimacy, privacy
Creation – skills, work, feedback
Identity – belonging, groups, recognition
Freedom – autonomy, rights, dissent

What are your feelings about this list?

Write a poem expressing your needs. (You might like to use the Seurat painting, the Virginia Woolf extract or the Manfred Max-Neef list as a starting point.) Your poem could be in the form of a list (of your needs). There is something about the brevity of lists and the distance travelled between items that makes them so like poems they need little work to finish. Make sure you go beyond the basics that we all share to explore and express your own longings, desires, hopes, joys.

Lists can collect together feelings, sense impressions, intuitions, thoughts, objects, people. They can be random, in that disparate things and ideas are drawn together, but they are also specific because choices need to be made. Lists can take you on different routes from those usually dictated by the rational side of the brain. Don't try to develop any one idea but let a variety of 'items' come to you in no particular order. Then, if you like, look for connections!

Share your lists.

Does the expression of your needs pose any threats to other people? Can your needs be met without damaging other people?

Living with others must be worked at. What can we do when people's needs and wants don't fit together?

Read the poems *Things* by Paul Matthews on page 24 and *A way to think fragility* by Joy Mead on page 27.

Choose one item on your list and explore it more deeply in a poem, paragraph or short story. If it is abstract, embody it in something tangible. Try to 'show' rather than 'tell'. For example, you might show love by writing about a particular gift: a pen, a plant, the touch of a special person … Something quite frivolous like a bar of chocolate might show the need for comfort. In *A way to think fragility* an egg is used to *show* fragility. My daughter arrived home with this egg in her rucksack just as my cancer had been diagnosed.

Share your writing.

Think about why poetry is dangerous. Many writers around the world are prisoners of conscience or live in exile. Many have been tortured and killed by their governments. Why are oppressive regimes so frightened of poets? Is it because poets try to express what it is to be wholly human? Do they disturb those who find difference threatening, who are no longer able to imagine and create, who have lost their humanity?

Read *This poem …* by Elma Mitchell on page 28.

Towards a conclusion

The title of this workshop is from a poem by Kathy Galloway:

Let us be different

Let us be different,
Let us not be the same,
You will be you, I will be me,
Each of us has our own name.

You do things your way,
In the light you have found,
You must be true to what you know,
And stand on your own ground.

Until we can learn
To honour each other,
To hear and know what makes us real
We can't love one another.

But when that time comes,
Though many the flowers,
From different roots, we shall be shown
That one earth is ours.

Kathy Galloway

Additional resources for Section 1

Things

What I'll miss most when I'm dead is
things that the light shines on.
If there aren't wet leaves in Heaven
then almost I don't want to go there.
If there isn't the possibility
of silly particulars
like library cards on a table
then I almost don't want to go there.
Library cards – because here some happen to be.
I am a small Englishman in an infinite Universe
looking at library cards. That's funny.
In fact it frightens me.

I am in my room, surrounded by the things
which have somehow clung to my existence;
a picture of squirrels, a desk with inkstains
(it was my grandfather's before me),
a Buddha and a jar of Nivea,
a pottery lion lying among rose-petals.
These are my things. They comfort
and encumber me.

But Buddha, what about you?
Your sides are so sheer.
You gave all your riches away.
And can you still hold
on to yourself as a person?

Did Christ give up his things too?
He had a seamless garment.
The other things came when he needed them,
the coin in a fish's mouth,
ointment for his feet,
a crown of thorns.
Well, he didn't despise things.
He ate bread readily.
He loved the boats of his disciples.

And it's not just things we love
but one thing next to another –
this African Violet beside the tuning fork,
this pen in my hand
as the rain outside falls among Quinces.
These things have happened before;
but when I happen to be there
and notice the shape of the space between them
then a new thing arises in the universe.
This was unplanned.
This event without karma.

Angels, though infinitely greater than us,
know nothing of this.
But Christ knows it.
He came for that purpose –
to write on a particular ground
with his little finger.

The Gods have enough of immortality
and need things.
They need cuckoos in a Damson tree,
they need Rhubarb flapping beside a gate.
Their paternoster is an honest man
who can hammer a nail straight.

Paul Matthews

A way to think fragility

(For Catherine)

A blown egg, decorated
with the blue of the darkest night
and a filigree of white; flowers
for a wedding, or a funeral.

You handled it with care;
trusted its endurance;
treasured it from an Easter Tree
in Prague
across a continent
quietly home.

Then lovingly, like the giving back
of life,
and the passing on
of hope
you offered
into my hands
a way to think
fragility.

Joy Mead

This poem ...

This poem is dangerous: it should not be left
Within the reach of children, or even of adults
Who might swallow it whole, with possibly
Undesirable side-effects. If you come across
An unattended, unidentified poem
In a public place, do not attempt to tackle it
Yourself. Send it (preferably in a sealed container)
To the nearest centre of learning, where it will be rendered
Harmless, by experts. Even the simplest poem
May destroy your immunity to human emotions.
All poems must carry a Government warning. Words
Can seriously affect your heart.

Elma Mitchell

Two

Speaking peace

Speaking peace

Aim:

To explore imagery and hidden messages; to search for a language of peace.

Preparation:

You will need:
- Pens and paper
- A flip chart
- 'Pebbles' cut out of thin card

Welcome:

Make sure people know one another and are at ease. Be ready to serve tea and coffee.

A beginning:

How do we 'speak' peace? How do we change from using violent imagery to using peaceful imagery?

Toys, games and free gifts offered with food products – for example, space weapons and Star Wars characters – may have an ethos of violence that goes unnoticed. **Talk about this. Name some other examples** ('soldier' growth charts?). It's happening in our schools, too. In some schools, caterers have been encouraged to give vegetables militaristic names to persuade young children to eat them. In some primary schools these include 'carrot spears' and 'potato cannon balls' to go with a 'grilled gladiator burger'.

(Information taken from Saying no to violence, *Peace Pledge Union)*

What is this imagery encouraging?

Can we go on ignoring the violence built into society, yet still attempt to teach children the way of peace and non-violence? How are we to create a culture of peace?

A new use of language has been brought into being to soften the reality of war. Bombing military targets in the hearts of cities is called 'denying the enemy an infrastructure'. People are 'soft targets'. Saturation bombing is 'laying down a carpet'.

We do this sort of thing to everyday language. Think about such expressions as 'a loving slap', 'punching the message home', 'targeting people'.

How many other such phrases can you think of? How do you feel about them?

Look for other military expressions in everyday use. Talk about their hidden influences. What is this use of language actually doing?

Also think about euphemisms, advertising language, conflations (sex and violence – why together?). Jargon is often used to control our imaginations and cover up flesh and blood suffering.

President Truman said of the bombing of Hiroshima and Nagasaki, as 15,000 people lay dead or dying from radiation: 'The experiment has been an overwhelming success.'

So much has changed in our world since that time – except, it seems, our thinking.

War films, war games

War is considered good entertainment: Why are war films popular?

Do people know the difference between fantasy and reality?

When television pictures were shown live from the cockpits of American planes homing in on targets during the Gulf War, more than one commentator noted how it was 'just like a computer game'. Have we lost the ability to imagine creatively and compassionately?

Memorials and ceremonies

Talk about the imperialistic, dominant, often phallic imagery of war memorials. Military ceremonies provide yet more images of war as an inevitable part of life: there was an enemy and the only way to defeat it was by fighting – our troops were 'successful' in resolving the conflict (despite the fact that millions of people died). Emphasis on patriotism, heroism and sacrifice is designed to leave us feeling grateful that we have our brave armed forces to fight on our behalf. Think about the personal and political implications of war – are they different and separate? Why are we prepared to act as a country in a way we would condemn in a person? Why do we tolerate, even admire, institutional ruthlessness, aggression, greed, violence, emotional destructiveness, killing? 'My dad hates violence but he says war is different' – Is it? Why? How?

The language of peace?

Sometimes it seems as if, as a community, we do not know the words with which to think peace? Why do so many people assume that the natural way to resolve conflicts is by violence and war, and so reduce the concept of peace to nothing more than preparation for war? It need not be so … it should not be so. War is not inevitable … neither is violence … in language and living … practice and poetry.

Peace does not just happen because nothing else is happening – it is not an end, something to work towards. It is a way of being.

Think about peace as active – as creative. Drama, painting, craft, creative listening, all co-operative activities, are peacemaking.

Read:

Jim Garrison, an American theologian, once told this story:

A monk had a dream. He was walking down a street when an aeroplane flew overhead and dropped a bomb. Instinctively everyone knew it was a nuclear weapon, and all scattered – except the monk. He felt he must catch the bomb before it exploded and destroyed everyone. He caught it, and the bomb turned to bread in his hands. He broke the bread and shared it, seeking out those who had run away and drawing them back into community.

Think about this story. It's not about magic. What is it about?

Swords into ploughshares

Mozambique suffered immensely from the small arms trade during its 16-year-long civil war. Since a peace agreement between government and rebel troops was signed in 1992, Mozambique has been destroying illegally held weapons.

An extraordinary project, backed by Christian Aid, has been set up to tackle this problem at community level. The 'Transforming Arms into Ploughshares' programme has collected and destroyed more than 200,000 guns, grenades and rocket-launchers. The weapons are handed over in exchange for farm tools, like hoes, and for other useful things, most commonly sewing machines, bicycles, and a vast array of construction materials. Mozambican artists from Nucleo de Arte then use the fragments of the destroyed weapons to create works of art. Weapons are fashioned into human forms, animals, birds, chairs, musical instruments ... These are exhibited in public places and sold to support the project's operations.

In 2001/2002, Christian Aid presented an inspiring collection of these sculptures. The exhibition, *Swords into Ploughshares*, was a powerful expression of the Mozambicans' ability to build peace and prosperity after years of conflict.

(Story of the Nucleo de Arte *taken from Christian Aid's website)*

Think about the imagery at work here. Look at the symbolic activities pictured on pages 36 and 37.

What is this imagery encouraging?

Take time to think of peace words. Write your peace words on the 'pebbles' then make a pathway with them (create a peace memorial?). Think about the words you have written. Are the words of your path passive or active? Personal or political? Can the personal and political be separated?

Words about peace are mostly abstract: truth, equality, human rights, justice ... yet wars are usually about tangibles like land, water, oil ... Think about how peace concepts are given 'body' in art and poetry. Now choose a 'pebble' and write a poem based on it. The word on the 'pebble' is probably abstract. Give it body and context by choosing, as the subject of your poem, something from your own experience: a garden, a wall, a child. For example, if the word is 'trust' you might like to write of a child's hand in yours; if it is 'beauty' you might like to describe the lines on an old woman's face. Try to make your connections different, unusual. They'll have more impact that way!

Share your poems.

Towards a conclusion

Peace is not a thing to possess, but a way of possessing;
Peace is not a gift to be given, but a way of giving;
Peace is not a topic to teach, but a way of teaching;
Peace is not a theory to learn, but a way of learning;
Peace is not an opinion to hold, but a way of holding;
Peace is not a resolution of strife, but a way of striving;
Peace is not a creed to preach; but a way of preaching;

Peace is not a God to serve, but a way of serving;
Peace is not a question to ask, but a way of asking;
Peace is not an answer to seek, but a way of seeking;
Peace is not a journey's end, but a way of journeying.

Richard Skinner

Anti-war toys event, Hampstead Heath, London, May 1996

Turning toys into musical instruments

Three

One-word answers ... or questions?

One-word answers ... or questions?

Aim:

To think again about words and the way we use them by exploring some one-word examples.

Preparation:

You will need:

- These words written separately on large cards:

   Time, Black, Girl, Poor, Progress, Development, Old woman

- A flip chart
- Pens and paper

Welcome:

Make sure people know one another and are at ease. Be ready to serve tea and coffee.

Introduction:

'There is nothing either good or bad, but thinking makes it so,' says Hamlet in Act 2, Scene 2 of Shakespeare's play.

In this workshop, we will pay close attention to a few individual words in order to think more deeply about how we use them. Often, we are unaware of the messages we are passing on. Many more or less neutral words are 'loaded' and owned by the ideology of their time. Words can be used to oppress, mould, disguise cruelty, destroy. When freed, words can create, reconcile, transform, liberate.

Exploring words

(Note to Workshop Leader: Show the word-cards one at a time to the group and ask people for their reactions and first thoughts about each word. Write these words down on the flip chart.)

Use the resources and questions on the pages indicated below to further explore each word.

Time – pages 43–45
Black – pages 46–48
Girl – pages 49–51
Poor – pages 52–54
Progress and Development – pages 54–60
Old woman – pages 60–64

Do the resources and questions open up the words, widen thinking and make people feel differently? Encourage further exploration of these words and others.

Write poems or stories using the words. Choose one word at a time. You might write poems of protest, hope or possibility but try to root your ideas in something tangible. For example, if you chose the words 'progress/development' you might like to think about the development (changes in thinking and attitude) of someone living in the minority (so-called 'developed') world and how those changes affect her/his way of life. You could begin with something as simple as a Christian Aid or Oxfam collection envelope, or a jar of Nescafé.

Share your thoughts and writing.

Towards a conclusion:

Remember words have a life of their own – they have their own secrets. Use them with care and try to be aware of the messages you are passing on!

Additional Resources and Questions for Section 3

Time

Time is intangible, yet the language we borrow from different areas tries to persuade us that time is a commodity we can trade, hold on to, own, destroy.

We 'spend' time (using money language).
We 'invest' time (using the language of commerce and big business).
We have 'enough' time.
We 'run out' of time.
We 'steal' time (using the language of materialism).
We 'kill' time.

How harmful is this use of language?
– How does it seal out and limit imagination?
– How does it slant our thinking and behaviour?
– Where do cycles and seasons come in?

Read:

Ecclesiastes Chapter 3, verses 1–8

For everything its season; and for every
activity under the sun its time:
a time to be born and a time to die;
a time to plant and a time to uproot;

a time to kill and a time to heal;
a time to break down and a time to build up;
a time to weep and a time to laugh;
a time for mourning and a time for dancing;
a time to scatter stones and a time to gather them;
a time to embrace and a time to abstain from embracing;
a time to seek and a time to lose;
a time to keep and a time to discard;
a time to tear and a time to mend;
a time for silence and a time for speech;
a time to love and a time to hate …

I would pick more daisies

If I had to live my life over again
I'd dare to make more mistakes the next time.
I'd relax;
I would limber up;
I'd be sillier than I've been this trip.
I would take fewer things seriously;
I would take more trips,
I would climb more mountains, swim more rivers;
I would eat more ice-cream and less beans.
I would perhaps have more actual troubles
but I would have fewer imaginary ones.
You see, I'm one of those people

who lively seriously and sanely
hour after hour,
day after day.
I've had my moments
and if I had to do it over again,
I'd have more of them.
In fact I'd try to have nothing else –
just moments, one after another –
instead of living so many years ahead of each day.
I've been one of those people who never goes
anywhere without a thermometer,
a hot-water bottle, a raincoat and a parachute.
If I had to do it again I would travel lighter.
If I had to live my life over I would start
barefoot earlier in the Spring
and stay that way later in the Fall.
I would go to more dances,
I would ride more merry-go-rounds and ...
I would pick more daisies.

Nadine Stair

What do these pieces say to you about time?

Think about the difference between your experience of time now and your experience of time, say, twenty-five years ago (if you're old enough!).

Black

White comedy

I waz whitemailed
By a white witch,
Wid white magic
An white lies,
Branded a white sheep
I slaved as a whitesmith
Near a white spot
Where I suffered whitewater fever.
Whitelisted as a whiteleg
I waz in de white book
As a master of de white art,
It waz like white death.

People called me white jack
Some hailed me as white wog,
So I joined de white watch
Trained as a white guard
Lived off de white economy.
Caught an beaten by de whiteshirts
I waz condemned to a white mass.

Don't worry,
I shall be writing to de black House.

Benjamin Zephaniah

What are your feelings after reading/hearing this poem?

And what about this one?

Black

Show me the woman
that would surrender
her little black dress
to a white-robed clan
and I would show you a liar.

Not for their bonfire,
her wardrobe saviour
the number
in which she comes
into her own power.

Go to a funeral
in black and know
that the dead
beside the white candles
will not be offended.

Add amber earrings,
perhaps a hat or scarf or pink
and know you are ready –
for a wedding.
How black absorbs everything.

Stand around at a party
in black – you are your own artist,
your own sensual catalyst,
surprised to say the least
when black brings you

Those sudden inexplicable hostile glances.

Grace Nichols

The Women in Black movement

Women in Black is an international peace network. The network began in Israel in 1988, with women protesting against Israel's occupation of the West Bank, and has developed in many other countries. It's not a formal organisation but 'a means of mobilisation and a formula for action'. Women, dressed in black as a symbol of sorrow, demonstrate in silent protest against war and violence and in solidarity with women throughout the world.

(www. womeninblack.net)

Think about the poems White Comedy and Black alongside the story of the Women in Black movement.

There are complex connections being made here. Don't be tempted to simplify.

Girl

How often, even today, do you hear women, sometimes old women, referred to as 'girls'?

This is a complex use of language. It's about belittling women – making them little ... doll-like maybe?

Read this extract from Henrik Ibsen's play *A Doll's House*, written in 1879.

Nora, the main character, is caught in a trap built of the economic and social order of her time and of patriarchal language:

Nora: *It's the truth, Torvald. When I lived with papa, he used to tell me what he thought about everything, so that I never had any opinions but his. And if I did have any of my own, I kept them quiet, because he wouldn't have liked them. He called me his little doll, and he played with me just the way I played with my dolls. Then I came here to live in your house –*

Helmer: *What kind of a way is that to describe our marriage?*

Nora (undisturbed): *I mean, then I passed from papa's hands into yours. You arranged everything the way you wanted it, so that I simply took over your taste in everything – or pretended I did – I don't really know – I think it was a little of both – first one and then the other. Now I look back on it, it's as if I've been living here like a pauper, from hand to mouth. I performed tricks for you, and you gave me food and drink. But that was how you wanted it. You and papa have done me a great wrong. It's your own fault that I have done nothing with my life.*

Helmer: *Nora, how can you be so unreasonable and ungrateful? Haven't you been happy here?*

Nora: *No; never. I used to think I was. But I haven't ever been happy.*

Helmer: *Not – not happy?*

Nora: *No. I've just had fun. You've always been very kind to me. But our home has never been anything but a playroom. I've been your doll-wife, just as I used to be papa's doll-child. And the children have been my dolls. I used to think it was fun when you came in and played with me, just as they think it's fun when I go in and play games with them. That's all our marriage has been, Torvald.*

The word 'girl' isn't used – but think about it! And if you are about to say that things have changed since Ibsen's time, then why is the word 'girl', for a woman, still so widely used?

What are the wider political implications of the personal relation-ships in the play? Talk about this.

Then read this piece from the **Conference of European Churches**:

A woman's experience

I am taking part in an ecumenical conference. In my working group are eleven high ranking men and myself, a laywoman.

I am politely asked what I expect from the conference. I say that for me a new community of women and men in the church is important.

'Madam,' replies the Metropolitan, 'I did not come here to talk about problems relating to women.'

'Madam,' the bishop informs me, 'women have an important task and it is to educate their sons so that they become priests.'

'Madam,' says another bishop angrily, 'do you not realise that Protestant women are destroying the ecumenical movement?'

The cardinal says nothing about this matter.

The moderator – striving to be civil – closes the subject: 'Madam, I do not understand women – they hate men, you know!'

With difficulty, I keep my composure!

Next day at a reception – I have a glass of blueberry jelly in my hand – the moderator speaks to me once again: 'So what then is women's spirituality, tell me?'

I try to explain and remind him of a woman with ointment who expressed her faith and her love in a way which was wholly her own. My hands try to help me explain – and the blueberry jelly spills all over my dress.

That ends the conversation.

The toilet attendant tries to console me. She cannot know that I am not crying over my dress.

How do you think this piece connects with the extract from Ibsen?

Poor

'Poor' is another difficult and loaded word. It is often used pejoratively, to patronise and belittle people. 'Poor' is often solely associated with problems. Yet all over the world there have always been people who live in great simplicity without considering themselves 'poor'.

Being poor, or poverty, has been distorted to mean: without those things the rich world considers important. Poverty is not necessarily misery or starvation. Originally, poverty meant the voluntary acceptance of a materially simple and uncomplicated life and giving up unnecessary possessions. In the Christian tradition a monk takes the vow of poverty. The first beatitude of the Sermon on the Mount is 'Blessed are the poor, for theirs is the kingdom of heaven.'

The problem is not poverty, or poor people. It is injustice, human exploitation, conspicuous consumption and the destruction of the natural world.

Wolfgang Sachs says

… the remark slipped out: 'It's all very well but, when it comes down to it, these people are still terribly poor.' Promptly, one of my companions stiffened: 'No somos pobres, somos Tepitanos!' (We are not poor people, we are Tepitans.) What a reprimand! Why had I made such an offensive remark? I had to admit to myself in embarrassment that, quite involuntarily, the clichés of development philosophy had triggered my reaction.

'Poverty' on a global scale was discovered after the Second World War: before 1940 it was not an issue.

... Up until the present day, development politicians have viewed 'poverty' as the problem and 'growth' as the solution. They have not yet admitted that they have been largely working with a concept of poverty fashioned by the experience of commodity-based need in the Northern hemisphere. With the less well-off homo oeconomicus in mind, they have encouraged growth – and often produced destitution by bringing multifarious cultures of frugality to ruin. For the culture of growth can only be erected on the ruins of frugality; and so destitution and dependence on commodities are its price.

Is it not time after forty years to draw a conclusion? Whoever wishes to banish poverty must build on efficiency; a cautious handling of growth is the most important way of fighting poverty.

It seems my friend from Tepito knew of this when he refused to be labelled 'poor'. His honour was at stake, his pride too; he clung to his Tepito form of sufficiency, perhaps sensing that without it there loomed only destitution or never-ending scarcity of money..

Think about it: when did you hear anyone say 'I am poor'?

In her book *The Myth of Progress*, Yvonne Burgess writes:

We think we owe our livelihoods to economics and technology. But in fact we owe our very lives to the basic social values which our economics-obsessed culture treats with contempt. Our mothers looked after us as we grew up largely out of such non-economic values; and no matter how rich or well-insured or heavily policed we are, Westerners (particularly middle-class Westerners) would not be able to rest easily in our beds, or rely on our bank accounts, were it not for the impeccable social values of the poor, both here and everywhere else. Their decency, generosity, and restraint allow us to feel safe, even when we walk around their countries as tourists, carrying cameras worthy a year's cash income to them.

… We seriously underestimate how much we are indebted for our safety to the morality of the poor.

This was written in 1996 and times are changing. We no longer 'rest easily in our beds'.

Poverty is a human creation. Talk about what we can do to help alleviate poverty in the world. Share feelings and ideas about recovering our social values, creating support networks, rediscovering subsistence skills, living more modestly.

Progress/Development

These are loaded words, which naturally link.

They also link with the words 'poor' and 'time'. Think about these connections as you read the following pieces:

Following the second world war, at the United Nations, American President Truman redefined the world in terms of the 'developed', and the undeveloped. Much of the white world he defined as developed, while much of the coloured world as undeveloped. So at a stroke a new concept came into being; the word development took on a new meaning. It was now used purely in terms of an industrial economy. All manner of production must be industrialised: food, clothes, housing, and everything else. The economies of artisans, peasants, small farmers and traders were made retrograde, ineffi-cient, uneconomic, irrelevant, out-of-date and a cause of poverty. Economic growth became the new 'god'. Economies of scale became the new 'religion'. Development agencies became the 'missionaries' of materialism.

(from *You Are Therefore I Am* by Satish Kumar)

Many tribal cultures and peasant societies lived and still live without war, without corruption, without pollution, without nuclear weapons, without population explosions, without exploitation, without drug abuse. And yet we call them poor and uncivilised, in need of 'development'. The Western ideology of materialism is teaching them to consider themselves poor and making them struggle to become rich. The rich show images, through adver-tising, which make people feel inferior, inadequate and deprived. It is like an unwritten conspiracy to undermine.

(from *You Are Therefore I Am* by Satish Kumar)

Properly used the word 'development' means what one dictionary defines as 'a gradual unfolding; a fuller working out of the details of anything; growth from within.' Real community development – integral human development – should therefore be about enabling a community to become more fully itself. And that's the trouble with having a grand scheme imposed from the outside: it tends to permanently disrupt the very fabric of a place. As such, it ain't true development.

(from *Soil and Soul* by Alastair McIntosh)

Kuala Juru – death of a village

Here
intimations of death
hang
heavy in the air
Everywhere
there is the stench
of decay and despair

The river
strangled by
exigencies of industrialisation
is dying …
and nobody cares

The fish
in the river
poisoned by progress's vomit
are dying …
and nobody cares

The birds
that feed on the fish
in the river
poisoned by
progress's excrement

are dying ...
and nobody cares

And so
a once-proud village
sustained
for centuries
by the richness
of this river
dies ...
and nobody
cares

To that mammon
DEVELOPMENT
our high-priests
sacrifice
our customs
our culture
our traditions
and environment
and nobody cares

We blind mice
We blind mice
see what we've done
see what we've done

we all ran after
Progress's wife
she cut off our heads
with Development's knife
have you ever seen
such fools in your life
as we blind mice.

Cecil Rajendra

Some call that village 'poor'.

From *The Myth of Progress*:

A very different attitude to work is expressed in the following story, which I heard at a conference about these issues a few years ago. A Mexican carpenter, asked to make six carved chairs like the one in his workshop, gave the Yankee tourist a price that was well above six times the individual price. 'But you should give me a discount if I buy six,' the man protested. 'And who is going to pay me for my boredom?' countered the carpenter.

Our enslavement to the idea of Progress and to our own technological achievements has led us Westerners to put the man-made 'laws' of economics, or 'the market' above our own better judgement, our social morality and our enjoyment of life. We have alienated ourselves from our own deepest needs, and we have called this process of alienation Progress.

The above extract is very like this story from Anthony de Mello's book *The Song of the Bird*:

The contented fisherman

The rich industrialist from the North was horrified to find the Southern fisherman lying lazily beside his boat, smoking a pipe.

'Why aren't you out fishing?' said the industrialist.

'Because I have caught enough fish for the day,' said the fisherman.

'Why don't you catch some more?'

'What would I do with it?'

'You could earn more money,' was the reply.

'With that you could have a motor fixed to your boat and go into deeper waters and catch more fish. Then you would make enough to buy nylon nets. These would bring you more fish and more money. Soon you would have enough money to own two boats … maybe even a fleet of boats. Then you would be a rich man like me.'

'What would I do then?'

'Then you could really enjoy life.'

'What do you think I am doing right now?'

Yvonne Burgess again:

We need to learn to do less, and to stop doing things to others. We need to stop trying to control everything and learn to let progress happen, to allow the runaway train of freedom to come on down the track. It is coming anyway.

(In this context, even ethical investment can be counterproductive, if it persuades us that no damage is being done by our affluence, so we can hang on to our capital and reap the interest with a clear conscience. Of course,

ethical investment is probably better than unethical or don't care investment. But it scarcely breaks our cultural pattern of self-serving moral righteousness!)

... we in the West should not be worrying any more about how to promote development. It is more to the point to ask: 'How can we stop doing to others, and stop forcing others to do to themselves, what we have already done to ourselves in the name of Progress?' – that is, turning from a cycle of seasons and mysteries, celebrations and mourning, work and rest, eating and fasting, into a linear, economic seventy-year plan.

And finally:

Whether it is capitalism, or communism, both emerge from the same idea that the pursuit of self-interest is a natural force which drives history forward and brings about progress and development. But if we are ruled by this belief – there can be no end to conflict.

What do you really mean when you use the words progress and development?

Old Woman

What do you think people mean when they describe someone as an 'old woman' – when they use the words to describe a man, for example?

Witches or wise women?

In fairy stories and folk tales, old women are often depicted as foolish and muddled or as cunning and full of evil intent. But when we go back to explore these stories more deeply, we may begin to see something different. Many 'witch stories' are about discrediting female knowledge of birth and death, of healing and plant lore. Fairy stories and folk tales often reveal a society's fear of women, fear of their experience, wisdom and power – particularly menopausal women.

Memories:

Think about folk tales and fairy stories. How do you remember old women in these stories?

Talk about the number of women who were put to death for being 'witches' – another holocaust?

The story of the Cailleach in Celtic mythology:

The story of the Cailleach, or hag, in Celtic mythology is fascinating. She is an ancient woman whose wisdom is won from long life experience. She is the Celtic personification of life energy, keeper of the cauldron of wisdom, a shaper of landscapes who can change her shape from menacing old hag to reveal generous and beautiful forms. Above all, she is a survivor who knows what is going on, and becomes wise in the process.

The rugged mountain landscape of the Beara Peninsula in south-west Ireland – a wild and beautiful place washed by the Atlantic – is the sacred space of the Hag of Beara, who in Christian tradition becomes the nun of Beara, turning to Jesus and Mary for strength to face old age and death.

On the Beara Peninsula there stands a strangely shaped stone composed of metamorphic rock. Local people call this stone 'The Hag of Beara', and say that she turned herself to stone so that there would always be a Hag of Beara. It's also said that you can see in the stone not only the hag but also a young woman.

What is your reaction to this story? What does its symbolism suggest?

Now read this poem:

Faith mother

I feel your nearness more acutely now
old woman: the last to be freed
from cruel joke and mocking cliché.

No longer put to death as witch
but often confined as confused.
Your seeing is threatening

(at menopause they say
women often see the devil)

and stands in the way
of conformity to a pattern
in which the human body is beautiful
only if it is young, shapely
and smells good.

But like Sarah long ago
you can still laugh
at the overlarge egos
of old men
hungry for lost dreams.

Your inner beauty
is the mysterious wisdom
of a heart, as yet, unbowed.
Your long and earthy memory
holds the experience of ages
of seeing and being
of waiting and pondering
all things in your heart.

Your ancient understanding
could even now be our hope
and our salvation.

Joy Mead

'Long life is in her right hand; in her left hand inner riches and self respect.'
Proverbs 3:16

A wise woman is creative in her later life. She rejects the stereotypes of older women as burdens to society and themselves, as ill or cantankerous semi-humans in need of care and control. Even when she needs care, she continues to give care through attending to those around her.

Four

G-O-D

G-O-D

Aim:

To explore the way we experience the word 'God'; to explore the influence of imagery.

Preparation:

You will need:

- Pens and paper
- A flip chart

Welcome:

Make sure people know one another and are at ease. Be ready to serve tea and coffee.

Introduction:

Language about God plays a social and political role. It shapes our thinking and attitudes. The discovery of new and different images for God has the potential to change the way we live. It may be that after exploring many images and words we find that silence speaks more meaningfully – that emptiness is the most appropriate image. This workshop is not about learning a pre-existing language of faith, but about enabling one another to discover words to tell our stories or to enter into old stories and find ourselves there. In any group of people there is likely to be a wide range of beliefs, thoughts and feelings about God. Respect for where each of us is coming from will enable us to explore fully and honestly.

Talk about:

Much God-language gives grounds for suspicion. French feminist philosopher Julia Kristeva defined Christianity as *'the ultimate home of the Law of the father'* ...

Until fairly recently, Christianity borrowed its language almost entirely from male experience, using words and symbols drawn from society's ruling groups. God was imaged as King, a patriarchal head of family ...

Read the poem *What is a father?* on page 73.

How do you feel about the father image?

When Jesus taught his disciples to pray 'Our Father ...' he was suggesting a way of relating. (Jesus called God 'Abba', 'Daddy'.)

What have we made of this image? Talk about this for a few minutes.

Consider the well-known images, much used in the Bible and hymnody, of God as a warrior, a judge, a master – one who controls and commands.

In the past, such images made God the creator of the social order and validated religious traditions and oppressive legal and family systems. A male authority God was the perfect image for a male-dominated society.

Those in power were (in many places still are) seen as representatives and agents of God, so to challenge or change the order was to disobey or rebel against God.

Many hymns contain this sort of imagery – the imagery of might and power, chosen people with God-given rights, triumph and glory: 'Jesus is Lord' or 'Jesus, the Conqueror, Reigns …

Other hymns contain militaristic imagery: 'Fight the Good Fight', 'Onward Christian Soldiers' …

Talk about hymns with patriarchal, militaristic and violent imagery. Look for other examples. How do you feel about them? How are they dangerous? This violence is also directed against language.

Read:

Extract from *Women and Godtalk*, page 71.
I cannot call you Lord by Kathy Galloway, page 71.

Talk about your reactions to these pieces?
How do we create a culture of peace?

Reflect upon different images of God. You might contemplate: the ocean (or ocean bed), a wise old woman, the wind, the beating heart at the centre of the universe, warmth and coolness, gardener, weaver, artist … You might like to think of God as verb rather than noun – as process rather than object, becoming rather than being …

Here is a beautiful image, from song in praise of Allah, that is neither verb nor noun but something of both:

My body is like a rabah*
My heart is like a tambourine
Rhythm throbs in my veins
Every hair on my body
Sings one note
And that note is your name, God

Amir Khusro Dehlavi

* a type of stringed instrument

Think of your own images. Write these down on the flip chart.

Now, working individually, write a short paragraph incorporating your own image of God. Underline the essential words in your paragraph and shape the words into a poem.

How do you see yourself in relation to God when you contemplate and use this image?

Share your writing/poems.

Looking for different images for God is more than just playing with words. Why? What difference could the use of such images make to the way we live – to our families, our communities, our world, to our relationship with the earth?

Talk about this.

Towards a conclusion

Your enjoyment of the world is never right till every morning you awake in Heaven … till the sea itself floweth in your veins, till you are clothed with the heaven, and crowned with the stars.

Thomas Traherne (17th-century religious writer and poet)

Thomas Traherne knew that surprise is every moment … every baby born … every new leaf … every insight and inspiration … every grasshopper, every note of music … We don't know where it's coming from, this huge surprise of life. The point is not to know but to accept and love life with all its uncertainty.

Love life
from birth, new beginnings
and hello …
through washing floors
and painting portraits
to the words of death, sorrow
and … goodbye
for where there is love
of life – there is God.

Additional resources for Section 4

A colleague came back from a field trip recently and was telling us about the conversation she had had with a woman she had met. Nuzat was a strong woman with a violent husband and a determination to keep going. She described how, at the age of 12, she had been married to a much older man. She had not understood what was going on on her wedding night, but had found it a very unpleasant experience and gone the following day to complain to her mother. Her mother had said, 'This man is now your husband and you must treat him like God.'

Nuzat said, 'Well, if God is like that I don't like him either.'

(From *Women and Godtalk*, a talk given by Bridget Walker
at the Quaker Centre, St Giles, Oxford, 1993)

I cannot call you Lord

I cannot call you Lord
With undivided heart,
For though my love would stronger be
It cannot take the part

Of those who seek to rule
By force or evil word
And justify their deeds of pride
As from a Sovereign Lord.

Nor can I yet forgive
A Lord Omnipotent
Who sanctions women, children, prey
As if such things were meant.

And if I should attempt
To call you Lord of Hosts
From every battlefield rise up
A million slaughtered ghosts.

I cannot find the word
To fit this woman's hour,
That lets me praise the power of love
Not fear the love of power.

Yet Jesus is my Lord,
The Life for all who seek,
The Liberator of the poor,
The Servant of the weak.

But he with you is One;
Before my heart must break,
O God, who are not man, help me
Find word, for this man's sake.

Kathy Galloway

What is a father?

My friend Lisa
wants me to go with her
to church on Sunday.

I peeped inside once.
It was dark, with a funny smell.
God lives there, Lisa said.

She said that God
is like another father.

Why should she have two
when I have none at all?

Lisa's father
has a funny smell
and hot hands.

He tries
to cuddle
when I go to play.

Mary's father hit her mother.
Jane says hers is always grumpy.
David's father is important
at the Bank.

My mum says those churchy people
are no better than the rest.

I wonder
what sort of father
their God is.

Edna Eglinton

Five

Coming home

Coming home

Aim:

To celebrate home as a story we tell.

Preparation:

You will need:
- Pens and paper
- A flip chart

Welcome:

Make sure people know one another and are at ease. Be ready to serve tea and coffee.

Introduction

What is this emotive concept of home all about? Is it about nationalism? Or is it about commitment to, and rootedness in, the earth? Is it about a physical place, or about a country of the mind, a homeland of the heart? Is home about the end of yearning, or about the way we are with ourselves, with others, with all life, growing from a rooted place and reaching out – a way of being?

Clearly, home has a wide range of often vague meanings.

When there are so many imponderables; when there is change all around us, when all is flux, how then do we find a language of belonging?

The way we express what we feel about home matters. Yet how can we even begin to talk about home when we know so many people have no home? Bricks and mortar, country, a sense of who they are, are luxuries beyond their reach.

Our sense of community, where we belong, who we are, is bound up with the way we tell our stories. Our private moments of understanding – what some would call enlightenment – open out and become part of something bigger as we find our words to tell our own story. The personal is always political. Our becoming who we are, the development of our humanity, is dependent upon how we listen to the stories of others who are also becoming who they are – many stories in the one story.

Try to discover your own language for home. What comes to mind when you hear the word 'home'? Talk about this. Collect significant words on the flip chart. Are the words about bricks and mortar or about sensibilities?

Home might be about looking at how we live – and how we want to live.

Dreams of home

A project worker provides children of Western Sahara (now living as refugees in the desert), Spanish children, and children living in Tower Hamlets, London with e-mail facilities so they are able to share their personal experiences. They tell of their 'dream city'. It has houses in the trees, transport by horse and elephant, and vines to swing on from house to house. There are no cars and no men ...

(from the article City of dreams and surprises, Connect, The Methodist Magazine, *Winter 1996)*

A UNICEF Statement details the needs of children:

Children have nearly the same wishes no matter where they come from. They want clean water to drink and enough food to eat. They do not want to be sick. They want space in which to learn, develop and play. They want to know their neighbours. Especially in cities, they want peace and safety from threats and violence. And they tell us that they want to collaborate with adults to make their world better. When children's interests are at the centre of a society's concerns, that society becomes humane. When forgotten, the society is thrown off balance.

What do you particularly notice in these two short pieces?
What do the children's wants and needs say about the meaning of home?

In a social survey conducted in 1995, the replies of 46,000 women gave this information:

Women want an end to all war and violent conflict and they are in no doubt about how this should be achieved. They want an end to the manufacture and trade of all arms and weapons, including nuclear weapons; they want negotiation and co-operation to be used to resolve conflicts instead of fighting and they want more women involved in the peacekeeping process. They want a move away from aggression and machismo, which they feel is the cause of war, and emphasis placed on increased tolerance and respect for others.

Now read this piece by Virginia Woolf:

... if you insist upon fighting to protect me, or 'our' country, let it be under-stood, soberly and rationally between us, that you are fighting to gratify a sex instinct which I cannot share; to procure benefits which I have not shared and probably will not share; but not to gratify my instincts, or to protect

either myself or my country. For, the outsider will say, 'in fact, as a woman, I have no country. As a woman I want no country. As a woman my country is the whole world.' And if, when reason has said its say, still some obstinate emotion remains, some love of England dropped into a child's ears by the cawing of rooks in an elm tree, by the splash of waves on a beach, or by English voices murmuring nursery rhymes, the drop of pure, if irrational, emotion she will make serve her to give to England first what she desires of peace and freedom for the whole world.

(from *Three Guineas*, Virginia Woolf)

This was published in 1938. What does it say to you today?

Look at these words from a Shaker song (tune: 'Lord of the Dance'/ traditional Shaker melody)

'Tis the gift to be simple, 'tis the gift to be free,
'Tis the gift to come down where we ought to be,
And when we find ourselves in the place just right
'Twill be in the valley of love and delight.

When true simplicity is gained
To bow and to bend we shan't be ashamed;
To turn, turn will be our delight
Till by turning, turning we come round right

Sometimes thoughts of home take us back to a golden time in the past. Longing for some other time and place (nostalgia) is a very demanding pain which fills us with the need to escape. Does that make our memories home – living in the past – or might home be about remembering a lost home or a country we've had to leave? We need to find words for belonging that avoid nostalgia and escapism. Right at the heart of the struggle for home lies the struggle for the way the story of place is told.

Salman Rushdie calls his intellectual and personal odyssey *Imaginary Homelands*. Home is a story: a country of the mind and memory we bear within us. The peace of belonging isn't fixed or final. It's organic – the still place, the growing place, always changing. Tomorrow is different and always will be. Peace isn't the end of yearning and uncertainty, but the opportunity to hope and work for the things we need and want, to find our home/where we belong/'the place just right' within community and relationship, language and story.

Do you see 'the place just right' as a physical place – room, house, shelter, country, state – or as a state of mind, a homeland of the heart, a way of being?

Is our story one about possession of property or about our place on this fragile, finite planet? Is ours a story that sustains life or threatens it?

Talk about this.

Read this blessing by Rosie Miles:

Blessing for a home

I've come to know a place I can call home:
It walls me gently round, it gives me space,
It offers me stillness, it contains my fears,
It roofs me safely under, gifts me grace,
It is both books and art, colour and light,
It shelves and stacks me, my life storage space;
It's work and love and dust and green growing things,
It's laughter, friends and food, it's cat's own place,
It is so full of me and all I am,
I've come to know a home, a sacred space.

Rosie Miles

Write your own poem using one line from this blessing. Use the image in your chosen line to explore and develop thoughts of home, homelands and belonging to the earth. Bring in more images. Use all your senses. Think about smells. Try to keep your poem rooted and resist the temptation to wander into abstracts.

Share your writing; tell your own story; listen to the stories of others. Might poetry help provide us a space where restlessness and alienation from self and place are resisted and we know ourselves at home?

Peace is being at home with who you are, where you are, and recognising and respecting this need in others.

Peace is loving life as we live it, treasuring and experiencing it in all its diversity and wholeness, knowing that all things that happen give birth to words, images and thoughts – stories – which could change our lives and go on doing so for ever.

Peace is a willingness to live lightly, with hope, joy and unknowing.

Peace is a living thing.

Look after it.

Towards a conclusion

It is out of being and accepting our uselessness
    that we can act effectively.
It is out of knowing ourselves in solitude
    that we are able to relate deeply to others.
It is out of receiving with open hands
    that we are able to give with open hearts.
It is out of our inner silence and wordlessness
    that we can speak with truth and passion.
It is out of reconciling tension within ourselves
    that we may heal tensions around us.
It is out of our hearing and understanding
    that we can be trusted as friends and ambassadors.

Kate Compston

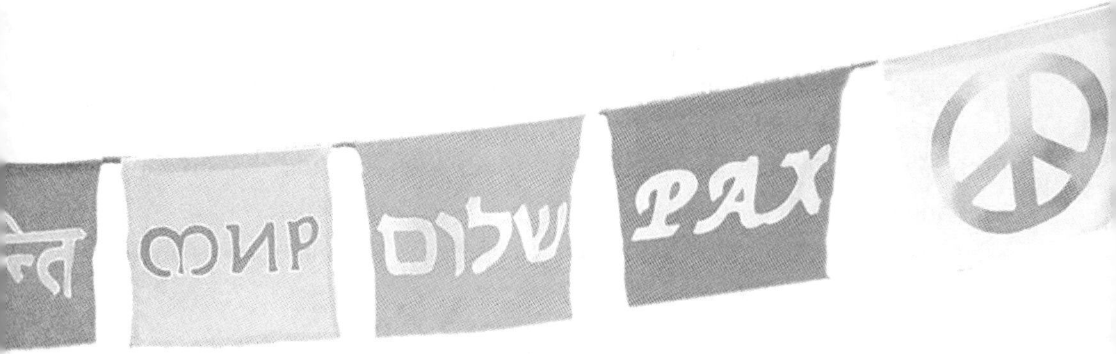
МИР
שלום
PAX

Making peace

A voice from the dark called out,
       'The poets must give us
imagination of peace, to oust the intense, familiar
imagination of disaster. Peace, not only
the absence of war.'
       But peace, like a poem,
is not there ahead of itself,
can't be imagined before it is made,
can't be known except
in the words of its making,
grammar of justice,
syntax of mutual aid.
       A feeling towards it,
dimly sensing a rhythm, is all we have
until we begin to utter its metaphors,
learning them as we speak.
       A line of peace might appear
if we restructured the sentence our lives are making,
revoked its reaffirmation of profit and power,
questioned our needs, allowed
long pauses ...

A cadence of peace might balance its weight
on that different fulcrum; peace, a presence,
an energy field more intense than war,
might pulse then,
stanza by stanza into the world,
each act of living
one of its words, each word
a vibration of light – facets
of the forming crystal.

Denise Levertov

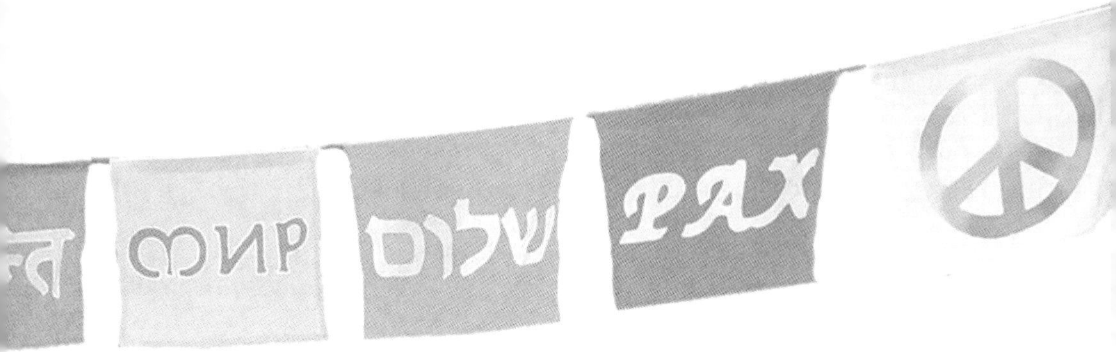
МИР
שלום
PAX

Sources and acknowledgements

Every effort has been made to trace copyright holders of all items reproduced in this book. We would be glad to hear from anyone whom we have been unable to contact so that any omissions can be rectified in future editions.

Section 1 – Let us be different

Extract from 'Kew Gardens' by Virginia Woolf included in *The Complete Shorter Fiction* of Virginia Woolf, The Hogarth Press, London, 1985.

Extract ('On the bottom') from *If This is a Man (Survival in Auschwitz)* by Primo Levi, translated by Stuart Woolf, © 1959 by Orion Press, Inc., © 1958 by Giulio Einaudi editore SPA. (p. 33) Used by permission of Viking Penguin, a division of Penguin Group (USA) Inc. Published in the UK by Bodley Head. Used by permission of The Random House Group Ltd.

Extract from *The Needs of Strangers* © Michael Ignatieff, Chatto and Windus, London, 1984. (p. 142) Used by permission of The Random House Group Ltd and of Viking Penguin, a division of Penguin Group (USA) Inc.

'Nine basic needs' by Manfred Max-Neef quoted in *The Little Earth Book* by James Bruges, Alistair Sawday Publishing Co. Ltd., Bristol, 2000. (p. 87)

'Let us be different' and 'I cannot call you Lord' by Kathy Galloway, from *Love Burning Deep*, SPCK, London, 1993. (pp. 66, 20) (Republished in *The Dream of Learning Our True Name*, Kathy Galloway, Wild Goose Publications, 2004.)

'Things' from *The Ground That Love Seeks* by Paul Matthews, Five Seasons Press, Hereford, 1996. Also included in *Earth Songs*, edited by Peter Abbs, Green Books Ltd, Devon, 2002. (pp. 78, 79)

'This poem …' by Elma Mitchell, from *People etcetera*, Peterloo Poets, 1987. (p. 60) *People etcetera* available for £7.95, post free, from Peterloo Poets, 2 Kelly Gardens, The Old Chapel, Sand Lane, Calstock, Cornwall, PL18 9SA, UK.

Section 2 – Speaking peace

Information from *Saying no to violence* edited by Jan Melchar and Margaret Melicharova, Peace Pledge Union, London, 2000. (p. 14)

'Peace is not a thing to possess' by Richard Skinner, from *Prayers for Peacemakers*, edited by Valerie Flessati, Kevin Mayhew Ltd, Bury St Edmunds, 1988. (p. 97)

Photographs: 'Disarming kids – converting war toys in London' from *Peace Matters*, magazine of the Peace Pledge Union, London, Summer, 1996.

Section 3 – One-word answers … or questions?

'If I had to live my life over again', Nadine Stair, from *The New Internationalist* (magazine), February, 1995. (This poem has also been attributed to Don Herold, Jorge Luis Borges, Brother Jeremiah, among others.)

'White Comedy' by Benjamin Zephaniah, from *Propa Propaganda*, Bloodaxe Books Ltd, Newcastle upon Tyne, 1996. (p. 14)

'Black' by Grace Nichols, from *Sunris*, Virago Press, 1996. Used by permission of Curtis Brown Ltd on behalf of Grace Nichols. (p. 10)

Extract from *A Doll's House*, Henrik Ibsen, translated by Michael Meyer, Methuen Drama, London, 1965. (pp. 98, 99)

'A woman's experience' taken from *Dare to Dream* by the Council for World Mission © Used by permission of Zondervan. (pp. 92, 93)

Extract from 'The discovery of poverty,' Wolfgang Sachs, *The New Internationalist* (magazine), No. 232, June 1992. www.newint.org

Extracts from *The Myth of Progress*, by Yvonne Burgess) Wild Goose Publications, Glasgow, 1996. (pp. 125, 212)

Extracts from *You Are Therefore I Am* by Satish Kumar, Green Books, Devon, 2002. (pp. 114 , 116)

Extract from *Soil and Soul* by by Alastair McIntosh, Aurum Press, London, 2001. (p. 151)

'Kuala Juru – death of a village' by Cecil Rajendra, from *Dove on Fire*, WCC Publications, Risk Series, World Council of Churches, Geneva. 1987. (pp. 53, 54)

'The Contented Fisherman' from *The Song of the Bird*, © Anthony de Mello S.J. 1982 by Anthony de Mello. (pp. 133, 134) Used by permission of Doubleday, a division of Random House Inc, New York, and by permission of Rev. J. Francis Stroud, Centre for Spiritual Exchange, New York.

Section 4 – G-O-D

'My body's like a rabah' by Amir Khusro Dehlavi, 13th-century Sufi poet, source of English translation unknown.

Extracts from *Centuries*, numbers 28 and 29 by Thomas Traherne, Mowbray, London and Oxford, 1960. (p. 14)

Extract from *Women and Godtalk*, a talk given by Bridget Walker at the Quaker Centre, St Giles, Oxford in 1993.

'What is a father?' from *How Are Your Spirits* by Edna Eglinton, The Old School Press, Devon, 2001. Also appeared in *Christian* magazine November/December 1989. (Magazine no longer published.)

Section 5 – Coming home

Photograph of William at home, by Joy Mead.

Extract from *Three Guineas* by Virginia Woolf, The World's Classics, 1992, Oxford University Press, Oxford. (pp. 312, 313) Used by permission of The Society of Authors on behalf of the Estate of Virginia Woolf. In the USA, copyright 1938 by Harcourt, Inc. and renewed by Leonard Woolf. Reprinted by permission of the publisher.

'Tis the gift to be simple', traditional Shaker song.

'Blessing for a home' by Rosie Miles, from *A Book of Blessings*, edited by Ruth Burgess, Wild Goose Publications, Glasgow, 2002. (p. 74)

'It is out of being. . .' by Kate Compston, from the resource pack *Textures of Tomorrow*, The United Reformed Church, 1996.

Final poem

'Making Peace' from *Breathing the Water* by Denise Levertov, Bloodaxe Books Ltd, Newcastle upon Tyne, 1988. (p. 41)

Cover picture – peace flags

The string of peace flags featured on the cover of this book is designed and sold by Karuna Arts in Hawaii. The various kinds of prayer flags they produce focus on honouring many different spiritual traditions, and encouraging world peace, multicultural awareness and religious harmony.

http://www.karunaarts.com

The Iona Community

The Iona Community, founded in 1938 by the Revd George MacLeod, then a parish minister in Glasgow, is an ecumenical Christian community committed to seeking new ways of living the Gospel in today's world. Initially working to restore part of the medieval abbey on Iona, the Community today remains committed to 'rebuilding the common life' through working for social and political change, striving for the renewal of the church with an ecumenical emphasis, and exploring new, more inclusive approaches to worship, all based on an integrated understanding of spirituality.

The Community now has over 240 Members, about 1500 Associate Members and around 1500 Friends. The Members – women and men from many denominations and backgrounds (lay and ordained), living throughout Britain with a few overseas – are committed to a fivefold Rule of devotional discipline, sharing and accounting for use of time and money, regular meeting, and action for justice and peace.

At the Community's three residential centres – the Abbey and the MacLeod Centre on Iona, and Camas Adventure Camp on the Ross of Mull – guests are welcomed from March to October and over Christmas. Hospitality is provided for over 110 people, along with a unique opportunity, usually through week-long programmes, to extend horizons and forge relationships through sharing an experience of the common life in worship, work, discussion and relaxation. The Community's shop on Iona, just outside the Abbey grounds, carries an attractive range of books and craft goods.

The Community's administrative headquarters are in Glasgow, which also serves as a base for its work with young people, the Wild Goose Resource Group working in the field of worship, a bi-monthly magazine, *Coracle*, and a publishing house, Wild Goose Publications.

For information on the Iona Community contact:
The Iona Community, Fourth Floor, Savoy House, 140 Sauchiehall Street,
Glasgow G2 3DH, UK. Phone: 0141 332 6343
e-mail: ionacomm@gla.iona.org.uk; web: www.iona.org.uk

For enquiries about visiting Iona, please contact:
Iona Abbey, Isle of Iona, Argyll PA76 6SN, UK. Phone: 01681 700404
e-mail: ionacomm@iona.org.uk